GIOACCHINO R[O...]

GUILLAUME TELL

Overture to the Opera

Edited by/Herausgegeben von
Lionel Salter

Ernst Eulenburg Ltd

London · Mainz · Madrid · New York · Paris · Prague · Tokyo · Toronto · Zürich

CONTENTS

Ernst Eulenburg Ltd
48 Great Marlborough Street
London W1F 7BB

PREFACE

Guillaume Tell was Rossini's thirty-eighth opera: it was also his last, for after its production in August 1829 he suddenly and unaccountably gave up composition almost completely, spending the remaining half of his life in masterly inactivity. Several reasons have been advanced – that his health was bad; that he was aware that his days of operatic supremacy in Europe were coming to an end and that Meyerbeer's star was rising; that with the 1830 Revolution and the fall of Charles X his contract to provide five new works for the Paris Opéra (of which *Tell* was the first and an opera on Faust was to have been the second) became null, and he lost all further interest; and that he was profoundly embittered by the public's indifference to what he considered, and other composers everywhere acclaimed as, his supreme achievement in the theatre.

It was probably the success of Auber's *Masaniello* the previous year – a story of a popular revolt which itself later provoked an insurrection in Brussels – together with a new French dramatic version of Schiller's *Wilhelm Tell*, that confirmed Rossini in his choice of this story of Switzerland's fourteenth-century struggle for liberation. He had been studying the scores of Beethoven – who had earlier advised him to stick to *opera buffa* as being best suited to his style and temperament; and to introduce this large-scale historical opera, on which he had spent nine months (as against a fortnight on *Il Barbiere di Siviglia*), he departed from his customary procedures and neither borrowed an overture from a previous work nor constructed one from themes from the opera itself. Instead, he composed a descriptive tone-poem, which falls into four sections.

A lyrical introduction, scored in highly original fashion for five solo cellos, supported only by the ripieni cellos and the basses, suggests the love of young Arnold for Matilda, the sister of the Austrian tyrant: it is twice interrupted by ominous growls of thunder from the timpani, but at its close a storm bursts which is more than the familiar phenomenon of nature in the mountains in that it also symbolises the fury of the Swiss under the yoke of their oppressors: the storm subsides and the *Ranz des vaches* is played on a cor anglais, echoed by the flute, which later adds birdlike warblings to the traditional Alphorn call; but this idyll is shattered by a trumpet signal which heralds an electrifying gallop (twice reaching a climax) that represents the surge of the Swiss towards liberty.

Editorial Notes

In preparing this edition the following early sources were examined:

A Rossini's autograph score of the opera (Paris, Bibl.Nat.MS 1331 R 17611)

B The original orchestral parts of the opera, used in the Paris Opéra 1829 (Paris, Archives de l'Opéra 4077)

C The earliest printed full score of the opera (Troupenas, Paris 1829-30)

D A lithograph full score of the opera (Ratti, Rome c. 1830)

E The printed miniature score of the opera (Ricordi, Milan n.d.)

Additionally, an early miniature score of the overture (Donajowski, London n.d.), the current scores and parts of the overture published by Schott and by Breitkopf & Härtel, and the previous Eulenburg edition of the overture were also consulted.

The cor anglais part, written in *A* in the old French tradition (i.e. in the bass clef an octave below concert pitch), is here printed in the now customary manner (i.e. in the treble clef a fifth above concert pitch), which in fact was already adopted in *B*. The somewhat misleading indication *Solo* often shown in the horn parts, and signifying merely that the passage was not to be played *a2*, has been replaced by a specification of which horn should play: likewise the marking *Solo* as applied to the triangle (i.e. not together with the bass drum and cymbals) has been avoided by showing the part on a separate line. For ease of reading, the cello clefs in the opening section of the overture have been restricted to treble and bass. The metronome marks are taken from *C*.

Despite the great popularity of this overture – indeed, perhaps because of it – the score as usually performed differs in numerous details from that actually written by Rossini. Many of these discrepancies are small, though by no means unimportant (length of phrasing slurs, presence of ties, precise placing of *crescendo* and *decrescendo* signs, etc); but some are major divergences, of which one of the most startling is encountered no later than b8, where, despite the unanimous evidence of the early sources, modern scores and parts have changed the first chord from a last inversion dominant seventh to a second inversion. This point at least admits of no ambiguity, but elsewhere the establishment of an authentic text bristles with problems. Rossini's score (*A*), obviously written at speed, is riddled with omissions, inconsistencies and even downright contradictions, quite apart from leaving continuations or repetitions of *sforzandi*, articulation marks (and it is impossible to be sure of the distinction, if any, between staccato dots and dashes) etc to be taken for granted; the orchestral parts (*B*) contain a number of obvious copyists' errors; and the first printed score (*C*) significantly differs in numerous details from both.

Doubts previously entertained about whether, since three trombones are demanded at only one point, the composer originally called for only two and momentarily forgot when he wrote the triad in b240, or whether he expected two of his three to play in unison almost throughout, are resolved by reference to *B*, where the latter is seen to be the case. The disposition of the cellos and basses is a lot less clear. In the auto-graph the two staves below the five solo cellos are bracketed together and marked *Violoncelli ripieni*; but in *C* and *D* these have become *Basses ripiennes* and *Primo e Secondo Basso* respectively. It is highly improbable that with five cellos already fully committed a sufficient number of cellos would have remained to allow them to be divided for a *ripieno*, and this is borne out in *B*, where the upper stave is allotted to the *ripieno* cellos and the lower to the basses - the disposition adopted for the present edition. The Opéra clearly had difficulty in meeting Rossini's requirements, for in *B* the solo lines have been re-allocated (rather clumsily) to three cellos and two violas dovetailed between them.

As was customary at the period, the string parts in *A* are, in general, given phrasing slurs rather than bowing marks – hence the apparently impracticable articulation for the cellos in the opening section; but when bowing does seem to be indicated it is often chaotically self-contradictory. Analogous passages are differently marked: in the Storm section the 'rumbling' semiquavers (e.g. bb58–62) are variously shown with two bows to a bar, one bow to a bar, or one bow to two bars, and moreover even when two string parts are in unison there is often no consistency between them – nor do the bowing indications in *B* tally with those in *A*. For the present edition it was decided, since no reason whatever could be adduced for such discrepancies, to adopt the most common pattern of one bow to a bar.

In other cases, inconsistencies have mostly been allowed to remain: on the face of it, the 1st cello's bowing in bb28 and 30 looks as if it should be identical with that in bb17 and 19, but the phrase extension from b27 upsets the pattern; we cannot know which phrasing Rossini really intended for the 1st cello in bb20 and 31, since each is quite unambiguous; he may or may not have meant the violins' $g\sharp'''$ in bb309, 345 and 353 to be sustained (although repeated in semiquavers in b301) or the upper winds' phrasing in bb117–118 to be mirrored in the bassoons, trombones and basses in bb118–119.

But extrapolation from these patterns, like any attempt to complete the erratically intermittent phrasing of the solo cor anglais part, immediately lands an editor in the realm of speculation and, in no time at all, leads to the kind of misleading distortions from which the score has already suffered. It is with the aim of showing, so far as possible, what Rossini actually wrote rather than what it is thought he meant to write, that this edition has been prepared: conductors and students may reach their own conclusions about the many debatable details of the score, but at least it will be on the basis of something approaching an 'Urtext'.

Grateful acknowledgements are made to the Bibliothèque Nationale and the Archive de l'Opéra of Paris, and special thanks are due to the BBC Music Librarian and her staff for their assistance.

Lionel Salter

VORWORT

Guillaume Tell war Rossinis 38. Oper. Sie war auch seine letzte; denn nach ihrer Uraufführung im August 1829 gab er unvermittelt und ohne erkennbaren Anlass das Komponieren fast völlig auf und verbrachte die ihm verbleibende Hälfte seines Lebens in meisterlicher Inaktivität. Dafür ist eine Reihe von Gründen angeführt worden: dass er bei schlechter Gesundheit war, dass er sich dessen bewusst geworden war, dass die Tage seiner Vormachtstellung als Opernkomponist gezählt waren und dass Meyerbeers Stern im Kommen war, dass mit der Revolution von 1830 und dem Sturz von Charles X. sein Vertrag, der Pariser Opéra fünf neue Werke zu liefern (von denen der *Tell* das erste war und eine Faust-Oper das nächste hätte sein sollen), gegenstandslos wurde und er so jegliches weitere Interesse verlor und schließlich dass er zutiefst verbittert war über die Gleichgültigkeit der Öffentlichkeit gegenüber dem, was nach seiner eigenen Meinung, und wie andere Komponisten weit und breit beifällig bestätigten, seine höchste Errungenschaft auf dem Theater war.

Es waren wahrscheinlich der Erfolg von Aubers *Masaniello* im Jahr zuvor – die Geschichte eines Volksaufstands, der später eine Revolte in Brüssel auslöste – sowie eine neue französische Dramatisierung von Schillers *Wilhelm Tell*, die Rossini bei seiner Wahl dieser Geschichte vom Befreiungskampf der Schweiz im 14. Jahrhundert den Ausschlag gaben. Er hatte die Werke Beethovens studiert – der ihm früher schon geraten hatte, bei der *opera buffa* zu bleiben, die seinem Stil und seinem Temperament am Angemessensten sei. So brach er für die Einleitung dieser groß angelegten historischen Oper, an der er neun Monate gearbeitet hatte (im Gegensatz zu den vierzehn Tagen für den *Barbier von Sevilla*), mit seinen gewohnten Methoden und übernahm weder eine Ouvertüre aus einem früheren Werk, noch baute er eine neue mit Themen aus der Oper selbst zusammen. Dagegen komponierte er eine illustrative Tondichtung, die in vier Abschnitte gegliedert ist.

Eine lyrische Einleitung, auf höchst originelle Weise für fünf Solo-Celli gesetzt, die lediglich von den Tutti-Celli und den Kontrabässen gestützt werden, beschreibt die Liebe des jungen Arnold zu Matilda, der Schwester des Habsburgischen Tyrannen: sie wird zweimal durch Unheil verkündendes Donnergrollen der Pauken unterbrochen, und wenn sie endet, bricht ein Sturm los, der mehr bedeutet als das gewohnte Naturphänomen im Gebirge, indem es gleichzeitig den Zorn des schweizerischen Volkes unter dem Joch seiner Unterdrücker symbolisiert. Der Sturm legt sich, und ein *Ranz des vaches* (Kuhreigen) erklingt auf dem Englischhorn mit dem Echo der Flöte, die später wie Vogelgezwitscher den traditionellen Ruf des Alphorns umspielt; doch diese Idylle zerbricht mit einem Trompetensignal, das einen elektrisierenden Galopp ankündigt (zweimal einen Höhepunkt erreichend), der die Woge der Schweizer auf dem Marsch in die Freiheit symbolisiert.

Revisionsbericht

Im Zuge der Erstellung dieser Ausgabe wurden die nachstehenden frühen Quellen kritisch durchgesehen:

A Rossinis Partiturautograph der Oper (Paris, Bibl.Nat.MS 1331 R 17611),

B die originalen Orchesterstimmen zur Oper, die 1829 an der Pariser Opéra verwendet wurden (Paris, Archives de l'Opéra 4077),

C die erste gedruckte Partitur der Oper (Troupenas, Paris 1829-30),

D eine lithographierte Partitur der Oper (Ratti, Rom ca. 1830) und

E die gedruckte Taschenpartitur der Oper (Ricordi, Mailand, undatiert).

Zusätzlich wurden noch eine frühe Taschen-partitur der Ouvertüre (Donajowski, London, undatiert), die derzeit im Gebrauch befindlichen Partituren und Stimmen der Ouvertüre aus den Verlagen Schott und Breitkopf & Härtel sowie die frühere Ausgabe der Ouvertüre als Eulen-burg Taschenpartitur herangezogen.

Die Englischhornstimme, in *A* noch nach alter französischer Tradition notiert (d. h. im Bassschlüssel eine Oktave tiefer als sie klingt) ist hier in der heute üblichen Notierung wieder-gegeben (d. h. im Violinschlüssel eine Quinte höher als sie klingt), was übrigens schon bei *B* geschehen war. Die ziemlich irreführende Be-zeichnung *Solo*, die sich so oft in den Horn-stimmen findet und lediglich besagt, dass die Stelle nicht *a2* zu spielen ist, wurde ersetzt durch einen Hinweis, welches Horn spielen soll; ebenso wurde die Bezeichnung *Solo* für die Triangel (d. h. ohne große Trommel und Becken) durch eine gesonderte Notenzeile für dieses Instru-ment vermieden. Um das Lesen zu erleichtern, wurden die Schlüsselbezeichnungen für die Celli im Eingangsteil der Ouvertüre auf Violin- und Bassschlüssel beschränkt. Die Metronom-bezeichnungen wurden aus *C* entnommen.

Trotz der großen Beliebtheit dieser Ouver-türe – womöglich gerade deshalb – weicht die Partitur, wie sie gewöhnlich benutzt wird, in zahlreichen Einzelheiten von dem ab, was Ros-sini tatsächlich geschrieben hat. Viele dieser Unstimmigkeiten sind nur geringfügig, jedoch keineswegs unwichtig (Länge der Phrasierungs-bögen, Bindungen, genaue Platzierung der *cre-scendo*- und *decrescendo*-Zeichen usw.). Es gibt aber auch einige größere Abweichungen, von denen eine der verblüffendsten bereits in Takt 8 anzutreffen ist, wo, entgegen dem eindeutigen Zeugnis der frühen Quellen, neuere Partituren und Stimmen den ersten Akkord von der dritten Umkehrung eines Dominantseptim-Akkordes zur zweiten Umkehrung abgeändert haben. Diese Stelle wenigstens lässt keine Mehrdeutigkeit zu, aber sonst bringt die Erarbeitung eines au-thentischen Textes eine Fülle von Problemen mit sich. Rossinis Partitur (*A*), offensichtlich in großer Eile geschrieben, ist geradezu durchsiebt mit Auslassungen, Unstimmigkeiten und sogar aus-gesprochenen Widersprüchen, ganz abgesehen davon, dass sie Weiterführungen oder Wieder-holungen von *sforzandi*, Vortragsbezeichnungen (wobei die einwandfreie Unterscheidung zwi-schen staccato-Punkten und -Keilen, wenn es sie überhaupt gibt, unmöglich ist) usw. als selbst-verständlich weglässt; dass die Orchesterstimmen (*B*) eine Anzahl von unzweifelhaften Kopisten-fehlern enthalten und dass die erste im Druck erschienene Partitur (*C*) in zahlreichen Details ganz erheblich von den beiden Quellen (*A* und *B*) abweicht.

Früher gehegte Zweifel, ob der Komponist, nachdem trotz der vorgeschriebenen Besetzung mit nur zwei Posaunen an einer Stelle drei benötigt werden, diesen Umstand momentan vergaß, als er den Dreiklang in Takt 240 nieder-schrieb, oder ob er beabsichtige, dass von diesen dreien zwei fast durchweg *unisono* spielten, werden behoben durch Bezugnahme auf die Quelle *B*, woraus zu ersehen ist, dass letzteres der Fall war. Die Aufteilung der Celli und Kon-trabässe ist wesentlich unklarer. Im Autograph sind die zwei Notenzeilen unter den fünf Solo-Celli zusammengeklammert und *Violoncelli ripieni* bezeichnet; aber in *C* und *D* sind daraus *Basses ripiennes* bzw. *Primo e Secondo Basso* geworden. Es ist höchst unwahrscheinlich, dass bei der ununterbrochenen Besetzung von fünf Celli noch eine genügend große Anzahl übrig geblieben wäre, dass sie sich für ein *ripieno* hätte teilen lassen. Das ist durch *B* erwiesen, wo die obere Zeile den *ripieno*-Celli zugeteilt ist und die untere den Kontrabässen – eine An-ordnung, die für die vorliegende Ausgabe über-nommen worden ist. Die Opéra hatte zweifellos Schwierigkeiten, Rossinis Anforderungen gerecht zu werden; denn in *B* sind die Solozeilen (recht unbeholfen) auf drei Celli und zwei dazwischen geschachtelte Bratschen umverteilt worden.

Wie zu jener Zeit üblich, sind die Streicher-stimmen in *A* im Allgemeinen eher mit Bögen für die Phrasierung als mit solchen für Bogen-striche versehen – daher die anscheinend unaus-führbare Spielweise der Celli im Eingangsteil; wenn aber damit die Bogenführung bezeichnet sein soll, dann ist das oft auf chaotische Art in sich selbst widersprüchlich. Analoge Stellen sind unterschiedlich notiert: Im Sturm-Abschnitt erscheinen die „grollenden" Sechzehntel (z. B. T. 58–62) einmal mit zwei Bögen für einen Takt, ein anderes Mal mit nur einem Bogen für einen Takt oder gar einem Bogen für zwei Takte, und darüber hinaus gibt es oft, auch wenn zwei Streicherstimmen *unisono* spielen, keine Übereinstimmung zwischen ihnen – noch entsprechen die Bogenstrichbezeichnungen in *B* denjenigen in *A*. Da für derartige Unstimmigkeiten keinerlei Begründung zu finden war, wurde für diese Ausgabe zugunsten des am häufigsten angewandten Schemas entschieden, nämlich für einen Bogen pro Takt.

An anderen Stellen wurden Widersprüchlichkeiten größtenteils belassen: Auf den ersten Blick erscheint die Bogenführung in Takt 28 und 30, als ob sie mit der in Takt 17 und 19 identisch sein sollte, aber die Fortführung der Phrase ab Takt 27 bringt das Schema durcheinander. Wir können nicht wissen, welche Phrasierung Rossini wirklich für das 1. Cello in den Takten 20 und 31 beabsichtigte, da eine jede für sich völlig eindeutig ist; er mag oder mag nicht beabsichtigt haben, dass die Violinen ihr gis''' in den Takten 309, 345 und 353 aushalten (wenngleich es in

Takt 301 in Sechzehnteln wiederholt wird) oder dass die Phrasierung der hohen Bläser in Takt 117–118 sich in Fagotten, Posaunen und Kontrabässen in Takt 118–119 widerspiegelt. Aber eine Fortführung solcher Schemata wie jeglicher Versuch, die uneinheitlich fragmentarische Phrasierung des Englischhorns zu vervollständigen, führt den Herausgeber unversehens in den Bereich von Spekulation und verursacht sehr rasch jene Art irreführender Entstellungen, unter denen die Partitur ohnehin schon zu leiden hat. Das Ziel, das diese Ausgabe sich setzt, ist zu zeigen, was Rossini tatsächlich schrieb und weniger, was er wohl gemeint habe. Dirigenten und Spezialisten mögen ihre eigenen Schlussfolgerungen aus den vielen strittigen Einzelheiten der Partitur ziehen, aber wenigstens wird sich das auf der Grundlage von etwas vollziehen, das einem Urtext nahe kommt.

Mit Dank für ihre Unterstützung seien erwähnt die Bibliothèque Nationale, die Archives de l'Opéra von Paris und ganz besonders die Leiterin der BBC Music Library und ihre Mitarbeiter.

Lionel Salter
Übersetzung: Ken W. Bartlett

Textual Notes

2, 7	*C, D, E*	Vc I n2 ♪not ♪
4, 9	*B*	Vc I beat 3 ♩. ♩
8	*all sources*	Vc II nl f♯'; Vc V nnl & 2 a & g
39-40	*all sources*	Vc ripieno octave lower than customary
40	*C, D*	Vc I whole-tone trill
42	*C, D, E*	Vc III n4 e
46-8	*D*	Vc V B throughout
48	*E*	Vc V e
76-7	*all sources*	Fg doubled by Cl not Ob
89, 90	*all sources*	Vla last note d'
91	*C, D, E*	Vla last note d♯'
92	*B*	Cor 4 e♭'
117, 119, 135	*B*	Tbni 1 & 2 nnl & 2 same pitch
126	*B, C, D, E*	Cor 3 & 4, n2 c" (unison)
134	*A*	Picc, Fl, Ob slurs ends on last note
143	*all sources*	Cl g'
145-7	*B*	Tbni 1 & 2 octave higher
147	*C, D, E*	Tbne 1 B
152-3	*B, D, E*	Ob octave lower
163	*B, E*	Cb B tied to previous note
176-225	*B*	C ing one slur per bar
191	*C, E*	Cl & Fg tacent until 192
	D	Cl tacent until 192
208	*C, D, E*	C ing last note a' (actual pitch)
240	*D*	Tbne 2 f♯' omitted
249, 257, 289, 297, 389	*B*	*sf/p*
252-9	*B*	Tbni 1 & 2 octave higher
292-9	*B*	Tbni 1 & 2 octave higher
306	*B, C, E*	Vla nl f'–c' (but not so in 350 except in *D*)
359	*B*	Tbni 1 & 2 octave higher
375	*B*	Cor 1 b'
399	*B*	Tbni as Vc
423	*B*	Tbni 1 & 2 octave higher
429	*A*	Fl octave lower
440-1	*B, C, D, E*	Ob & Cl tied
444, 447	*B*	Tbni 1 & 2 octave higher
448	*B*	Tbni 1 & 2 n2 octave higher
451	*B*	Tbni 1 & 2 nl octave higher
452	*B*	Tbni 1 & 2 n2 octave higher
453	*B*	Tbni 1 & 2 octave higher

GUILLAUME TELL
Overture to the Opera

Gioacchino Rossini
(1792–1868)

I. **Andante** (♩ = 54)

Edited by Lionel Salter
© 2011 Ernst Eulenburg Ltd, London
and Ernst Eulenburg & Co GmbH, Mainz

6

22

49

stringendo